THE BATHROOM TRIVIA BOOK

by

Russ Edwards & Jack Kreismer

RED-LETTER PRESS, INC.
Saddle River, New Jersey

ACKNOWLEDGMENTS

Project Development Coordinator:
Kobus Reyneke

Cover design and typography:
s.w.artz, inc.

Editorial:
Jeff Kreismer

Significant Others:
Theresa Adragna
Kathy Hoyt, Robin Kreismer
Jim & Rory Tomlinson, Lori Walsh

INTRODUCTION

For more than twenty years, the original Bathroom Library has entertained people on the go everywhere. With millions of copies out there, it proves that we're not all wet about bathroom reading.

Now, as heir to the throne, we proudly introduce a brand new Bathroom Library. We hope you enjoy this installment of it.

Yours flushingly,

Jack Kreismer
Publisher

**FOR AMERICA'S
FAVORITE READING ROOM**

THE
BATHROOM
TRIVIA BOOK

*Nuggets of Knowledge
for Commodious
Contemplation*

THE BATHROOM LIBRARY

RED-LETTER PRESS, INC.
Saddle River, New Jersey

FIRST THINGS FIRST

1. What was the first television game show in the U.S.?
   a) *The Price is Right*   b) *Truth or Consequences*
   c) *Name That Tune*   d) *Jeopardy*

2. Who was the first gorilla born in captivity?
   a) Mojo   b) Cojo   c) Coco   d) Reggie

3. The first Grammys on record were awarded in:
   a) 1943   b) 1958   c) 1963   d) 1959

4. Who was the first cartoon character blown up to be a parade balloon?
   a) Beetle Bailey   b) Felix The Cat   c) Mickey Mouse
   d) Betty Boop

5. What year saw the first seeing-eye dogs?
   a) 1947   b) 1963   c) 1938   d) 1929

6. When and where did the first skyscraper tickle the clouds?
   a) 1850, London   b) 1885, Chicago   c) 1890, Paris
   d) 1901, Cairo

7. He became the first person to become sole owner of a major motion picture studio when he bought RKO in 1954:
   a) Getty   b) Rockefeller   c) Hughes   d) Hearst

8. Where was the first artificial ice rink built in 1876?
   a) Chicago   b) London   c) Moscow   d) Iceland

9. What carmaker instituted a crash program and brought out seatbelts in 1950?
   a) Nash   b) Cadillac   c) Chevy   d) Packard

10. What was the first tropical storm named after a man?
    a) Bill   b) Bud   c) Butch   d) Bartholomew

ANSWERS

1. B: *Truth or Consequences* ... It debuted on July 1, 1941 with Ralph Edwards as the host and Ivory Soap as its sponsor.

2. B: Cojo

3. D: 1959

4. B: Felix the Cat

5. C: 1938

6. B: Chicago in 1885 ... It was ten stories.

7. C: Howard Hughes

8. B: Chelsea, London

9. A: Nash

10. B: Bud, on June 19, 1978

PRIVIA

If you're ever motoring through The Lone Star State, remember the Alamo Heights Toilet Seat Art Museum which displays 30 years worth of Barney Smith's greatest creations.

A.K.A.

1. In 1962, the "Galactic Network" was first conceived. What do we call it nowadays?

2. There was a popular British comedy in the '70s called *Man About The House*. By what name do we know the American version?

3. In 1929, it hit the shelves as Bib-Label Lithiated Lemon-Lime Soda. It has since had an image makeover and done fairly well for itself under what name?

4. He began life as a King and ended up as a U.S. President. Can you identify him?

5. *Head of the Family* didn't make it under its original name or star. This sitcom, which was bankrolled by Joseph P. Kennedy, was later picked up and eventually became a classic under what name?

6. It's the most widely sung song in the world but not under its original title, *Good Morning To You*. What's the title these days?

7. When it was first observed after World War I, Veteran's Day was known as_____?

8. Back in 1953, they still let the lab boys name products so the chemist who developed "Water Displacement, 40th attempt" called it exactly that but marketing boys tweaked it a bit to _____?

9. When first introduced, this bright idea was called "Light Amplification by Stimulated Emission of Radiation." What do we call this ubiquitous product nowadays?

10. What was Mario's original name in the *Super Mario Brothers* video game?

ANSWERS

1. The Internet

2. *Three's Company*

3. Seven-Up

4. Gerald Ford, born Leslie King

5. *The Dick Van Dyke Show*

6. *Happy Birthday*

7. Armistice Day

8. WD-40

9. Laser

10. Jumpman

POT SHOTS

Here's an important number to remember: there are seven loops in the squiggle atop a Hostess cupcake.

•••

A standard business card measures 3 1/2" wide by 2" long.

•••

Hippos can run faster than humans.

POTTY-POURRI

1. Blenheim, Lord Derby and Peasgood are all types of ...?
   a) Hats b) Apples c) Horses d) Pears

2. What was the name of the Flintstones newspaper?
   a) *The Daily Slate* b) *The Bedrock Herald*
   c) *The Dinosaur Gazette* d) *The Bedrock Times*

3. In what country was Mel Gibson born?
   a) Australia b) New Zealand c) United States d) England

4. What cartoon cat first appeared in the magazine *Feline Follies*?
   a) Top Cat b) Garfield c) Morris d) Felix

5. Who is Gordon Sumner better known as?
   a) Gordon Lightfoot b) Gordon of Peter and Gordon
   c) Sting d) Prince

6. What TV show made Fozzie Bear Famous?
   a) *Sesame Street* b) *Romper Room* c) *Muppets*
   d) *Barney and Friends*

7. Which of the following actors has not played James Bond's boss, "M"?
   a) Bernard Lee b) Dame Judi Dench c) Edward Fox
   d) Kenneth More

8. Brandophiles are:
   a) Cowboys who hot-stamp cattle b) Shoppers who refuse to buy generic foods c) Collectors of cigar bands
   d) Marlon Brando groupies

9. Whose picture was on the first U.S. postage stamp?
   a) Thomas Jefferson b) George Washington
   c) Benjamin Franklin d) Betsy Ross

10. What's the official name for that thing that's hit back and forth in badminton?
    a) Birdie b) Shuttlecock c) Racquetball d) Eagle

ANSWERS

1. B

2. A

3. C

4. D

5. C

6. C

7. D

8. C

9. C

10. B

POT SHOTS

In England, lady bugs are called lady birds.

•••

A librocubicularist is someone who reads in bed.

•••

Snails can sleep for three years without eating.

CAPITALIZING ON IT

What's the capital of Albania? The "A" of course.
Actually it's the city of Tirana. See how many of these other
lesser-known capitals you can match with their nations.

1. Ivory Coast
2. Sri Lanka
3. Bolivia
4. Costa Rica
5. Somalia
6. Marshall Islands
7. Barbados
8. Guyana
9. Yugoslavia
10. Liechtenstein

a) Georgetown
b) San Jose
c) Belgrade
d) Dalap-Uliga-Darrit
e) Colombo
f) Yamoussoukro
g) Bridgetown
h) LaPaz
i) Mogadishu
j) Vaduz

PRIVIA

A newspaper in St. John, New Brunswick, Canada,
once reported that a man was sentenced to
30 days in jail for stealing three boxes of Ex-Lax.
His name: Frederick Andrew Outhouse.

ANSWERS

1. F

2. E

3. H

4. B

5. I

6. D

7. G

8. A

9. C

10. J

POT SHOTS

Ever wonder why the portrait of FDR appears
on the dime? It's because of his work on behalf of
the March of Dimes and its battle against the
disease that crippled him, polio.

•••

Check out your typewriter or computer keyboard
and you'll notice there are three sets of letters in
alphabetical order: f-g-h, j-k-l, and o-p.

THE BREAKFAST CLUB

*Here's a Pop (as in Snap and Crackle) quiz
on some of America's favorite cereals.*

1. In 1877, this company designed the figure of a man which became the first registered trademark for a breakfast cereal. Can you name the company?

2. What breakfast cereal challenges you to "pinch an inch."

3. Who was the first female to appear on a box of Wheaties?

4. Toucan Sam, the Froot Loops mascot, originally spoke in Toucanese which is a form of what language?

5. What was the first ready to eat breakfast cereal?

6. What's the name of the character who puts "two scoops" in every box of Raisin Bran?

7. Which of the Rice Krispies brothers is the oldest?

8. Which is the odd one out and why?
   a) Frosted Flakes b) Rice Krispies c) Grape Nuts d) Froot Loops

9. What cereal maker was founded in 1866 and was originally called the Washburn-Crosby Company?

10. Name the cereal that has oats shaped like rainbows, horseshoes, hearts and clovers.

THOUGHTS OF THE THRONE

Hollywood is like Picasso's bathroom.
  -Candice Bergen

ANSWERS

1. The Quaker Oats Company

2. Kellogg's Special K

3. Mary Lou Retton

4. Pig Latin

5. Shredded Wheat

6. Sunny

7. Snap ... He was born in 1933 while Crackle and Pop made their first appearance in 1941.

8. C- Grape Nuts is made by Post. All the others are Kellogg products.

9. General Mills

10. Lucky Charms

POT SHOTS

Rubber bands last longer when refrigerated.

•••

Cinderella has been made into a movie more times than any other story.

WHAT'S IN A NAME?

Here's a bit of linguistic legerdemain that will test the vitality
of your vocabulary with these arcane appellations:

1. The little plastic tips of shoelaces?
   a) Holds   b) Toppers   c) Aglets   d) Fibbers

2. The two vertical lines that run from the top of your upper lip
   to the bottom of your nose?
   a) Frog   b) Chase   c) Ditch   d) Filtrum

3. Which of the following is not a word to describe the scribbles
   used to denote cursing in most comic strips?
   a) Babbles   b) Nittles   c) Grawlix   d) Jarns

4. The proper name for an armband is:
   a) Clayburn   b) Armcoat   c) Izard   d) Brassard

5. The indentation at the bottom of wine bottles?
   a) Belfrey   b) Bank or Boot   c) Heel   d) Kick or Punt

6. Small beadlike pieces of candy - usually silver colored - used
   for decorating cookies, cakes, sundaes, etc.?
   a) Codillions   b) Flitters   c) Blods   d) Dragees

7. The metal band holding the eraser to the pencil?
   a) Eraser band   b) Ferrule   c) Snype   d) Clip

8. The revolving star on the back of a cowboy's spurs?
   a) Tack   b) Stab   c) Star   d) Rowel

9. A faucet with a bent-down nozzle?
   a) Snozz   b) Woggle   c) Tap   d) Bibcock

10. The sharp part of a knife, which projects out from a handle?
   a) Shaft   b) Tang   c) Spear   d) Point

ANSWERS

1. C

2. D

3. A

4. D

5. D

6. D

7. B

8. D

9. D

10. B

POT SHOTS

"I am" and "I do" are the shortest complete sentences in the English language.

•••

There are more calls made on Mother's Day than any day of the year. There are more collect calls made on Father's Day than any day of the year.

TIMELINE

Place the events below at their proper place on the timeline.

A. "In God We Trust" becomes official motto of the United States

B. First e-mail sent

C. Customer rides first Ferris Wheel

D. First televised Olympics

E. *Peter Rabbit* first published

F. Spam is born

G. Income tax first withheld from Americans' paychecks

H. First genetically engineered crop

I. First ball point pen

J. First shampoo marketed in the U.S.

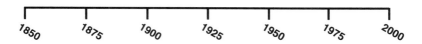

1850   1875   1900   1925   1950   1975   2000

PRIVIA

The Pentagon was built with twice as many bathrooms as necessary because, back in the 1940s, Virginia still had segregation laws requiring separate facilities.

ANSWERS:

A: 1956

B: 1971

C: 1893

D: 1936

E: 1902 (although Beatrix Potter created the character in a letter written in 1893)

F: 1937

G: 1943

H: 1982 (The Flavr-Savr tomato)

I: 1945

J: 1930 (Breck)

PRIVIA

Visitors to Buckingham Palace have reported that the queen has a diamond toilet seat with a marble base.

———

The White House has 34 bathrooms.

———

Actress Joan Crawford changed her toilet seats every time she changed husbands.

POTTY-POURRI

Have fun with this general knowledge trivia workout.

1. What simple idea did Tom Linson come up with that's now used billions of times a week by people around the world?

2. The Chinese have some 50,000 of them - or 49,974 more than we do. What?

3. Who was the first musical guest on *Saturday Night Live*?

4. Baloney was first served in Bologna, Italy. Is this statement factual or baloney itself?

5. What is the plural of the word "moose"?

6. What's the term for three consecutive strikes in bowling?

7. The old-fashioned name for this instrument is a claviar. What do we call it now?

8. What toy do arctophiles collect?

9. What well-known song did Katharine Lee Bates write in 1893?

10. What was the first novel ever written on a typewriter?

POT SHOTS

A pair of dice, or pips as they are called,
has a total of 42 dots.

•••

111,111,111 x 111,111,111 =
12,345,678,987,654,321

ANSWERS

1. Using the "@" as a locator in an e-mail address

2. Letters of the alphabet

3. Billy Preston

4. It's true.

5. Moose

6. A turkey

7. The piano

8. Teddy bears

9. *America The Beautiful*

10. *The Adventures of Tom Sawyer*

POT SHOTS

Carl Linder, the 1919 winner of the Boston
Marathon, was rejected for military service
because of flat feet.

•••

If you're a touch-typist, you might know that the
longest word that can be typed on a standard
keyboard using only the left hand is "stewardesses."

AMUSEMENTS

*Here's a wild roller coaster ride through Trivia World-
a real E-Ticket attraction -so stay seated
and keep your arms inside the vehicle at all times.*

1. Where is the largest indoor themed entertainment park in the United States?

2. Where was the first Legoland built?

3. What world record does Cedar Point Amusement Park in Sandusky, Ohio hold?

4. Purely by coincidence, Disneyland in California and Walt Disney World in Florida are in counties with the same name. What is that county?

5. What famous ride, invented in 1893 in Chicago, is named for its creator?

6. What is the name of the one loop steel coaster at Hershey Park, Pennsylvania?

7. Walt Disney World opened in:
   a) 1964   b) 1968   c) 1971   d) 1975

8. What amusement park was featured in the movie *Hairspray*?

9. What does EPCOT stand for?

10. What real amusement park doubled for Wally World in *National Lampoon's Vacation*?

THOUGHTS OF THE THRONE

*My family tree was chopped down and they
made it into toilet paper. We've never been closer.*

-Barry Steiger

ANSWERS

1. Camp Snoopy which is located inside The Mall of the Americas in Bloomington, Minnesota, sits under 1.2 miles of skylights, allowing 70 percent of natural light to enter the park.

2. Denmark is home to the first Legoland, a theme park built from plastic Lego blocks. It's Denmark's most-visited attraction outside of Copenhagen.

3. It has more rides, 68, and more roller coasters, 14, than any other amusement or theme park according to the book of *Guinness World Records*.

4. Both counties are named "Orange."

5. The Ferris Wheel ... George Ferris designed the giant wheel for the World's Columbian Exposition. It stood 250 feet above the ground and could hold 40 people.

6. The Sooper Dooper Looper

7. C

8. Dorney Park, Pennsylvania

9. Experimental Prototype Community of Tomorrow

10. Magic Mountain

PRIVIA

As upscale bath shop in London goes by the name "Plush Flush."

SNACK PACK

*You munch them, you crunch them
but how well do you really know them?*
Match the snack with the year it was introduced.

1. Fig Newton	a) 1921
2. Baby Ruth	b) 1902
3. Jell-O	c) 1896
4. Animal Crackers	d) 1897
5. Tootsie Roll	e) 1891
6. Planters Peanuts	f) 1929
7. Oreos	g) 1900
8. Hershey Bar	h) 1912
9. Mary Jane	i) 1964
10. Doritos	j) 1914

PRIVIA

The Sunday Independent, a Wilkes-Barre, PA newspaper, once reported a story about a woman who returned home after a hospital stay "and found the first-floor rear door to her home forced open. In a search of the home, the only article found missing was a four-pack of Charmin toilet tissue."

ANSWERS

1. E

2. A

3. D

4. B

5. C

6. F

7. H

8. G

9. J

10. I

POT SHOTS

Did you know that 40% of all the people who come to your parties snoop in your medicine cabinet?

•••

Q is the only letter that does not appear in the spelling of any of the 50 U.S. states.

•••

Four out of five people sing in the car.

FACTOID OR FALSEHOOD

True or false...?

1. In addition to the tides in the sea, the action of the sun and the moon also cause land tides.

2. Radio Flyer Wagons were so named because the company was owned by Guglielmo Marconi and Charles Lindbergh.

3. The stitches on a baseball are called "virgules."

4. Turtles can breathe through their backsides.

5. The answers inside a Magic Eight Ball are printed on a 20-sided figure.

6. Fats Domino never had a number-one hit.

7. The state of Florida is larger than England.

8. Harrison Ford is a descendant of Henry Ford.

9. Richard M. Nixon just happened to be in Dallas the day Kennedy was shot.

10. Bill Gates paid $1 million for the original Windows operating system.

THOUGHTS OF THE THRONE

I'm terribly lazy. That's why I love being in movies.
I'm performing all over the world -
while I'm home taking a bath.

-Barbra Streisand

ANSWERS

1. True

2. False ... The names were chosen for their (at the time) modern and cutting edge cache.

3. False ... A virgule is the slash between fractions (2/3) and words (and/or).

4. True

5. True, an icosahedron

6. True

7. True

8. False

9. True- but so were a million other people

10. False ... He paid only $50,000!

PRIVIA

Until December, 1978 a Connecticut regulation required all toilets to have horseshoe-shaped seats.

———

Late Beatle George Harrison had a toilet seat that played *Lucy in the Sky with Diamonds.*

THEMES FAMILIAR

You've heard them a zillion times but do you know their titles?
Here's a quiz to get your memory humming.
Identify the classic shows by their themes.

1. *The Toy Parade*

2. *Suicide Is Painless*

3. *The William Tell Overture*

4. *Funeral March of a Marionette*

5. *Bubbles In The Wine*

6. *Love In Bloom*

7. *Holiday For Strings*

8. *Londonderry Air*

9. *Fishin' Hole Theme*

10. *Home To Emily*

POT SHOTS

"Dreamt" is the only word in the English language
that ends in "mt."

•••

Mr. Rogers is an ordained minister.

ANSWERS

1. *Leave It To Beaver*

2. M*A*S*H*

3. *The Lone Ranger*

4. *Alfred Hitchcock Presents*

5. *The Lawrence Welk Show*

6. *The Jack Benny Show*

7. *The Red Skelton Show*

8. *Make Room For Daddy ("Oh Danny Boy")*

9. *The Andy Griffith Show*

10. *The Bob Newhart Show*

PRIVIA

On April 23, 1978 a 25 pound green iceberg fell from the sky and landed in Ripley, Tennessee. The Federal Aviation Administration later reported that the ice mass was frozen waste that had fallen from a leaky airplane toilet.

FORMERLY KNOWN AS

1. The Delicious apple was first named?

2. What was the game of Scrabble first called?

3. When Charles Schultz first penned his *Peanuts* comic he used a different name for it. What was the original title?

4. The classic toy Etch-A-Sketch was originally known as ...?

5. *Everybody Comes To Rick's* was the original name of the play. As a film it was re-titled ...?

6. Boriken was the original name of what island?

7. They were originally Leonard, Adolph and Julius but later gained fame under what name?

8. Years ago, if you chucked a "Pluto Platter" what were you doing?

9. The country of Iran was formerly known as Persia. What was it known as before that?

10. Who was born Marshall Mathers III?

POT SHOTS

IBM was once known as the
Computing-Tabulating-Recording Company.

•••

Harrison Ford turned down Tom Hanks' role in
Saving Private Ryan.

ANSWERS

1. Hawkeyes

2. Lexico

3. It was originally called *Li'l Folks*.

4. Magic Screen

5. *Casablanca*

6. Puerto Rico

7. The Marx Brothers- Chico, Harpo and Groucho

8. Throwing a Frisbee

9. Iran

10. Eminem

POT SHOTS

Snickers is the most popular candy bar.

•••

Mosquitoes are attracted to the color blue.

•••

It's impossible to lick your elbow. Go ahead- try it.

•••

The apple is the most popular fruit in the U.S.

NOTICE OPERANDI

How observant are you? Would you be able to hold your own with the likes of Holmes or Colombo? Here's a test to find out.

1. On the United States flag is the top stripe red or white?

2. Does the Pillsbury Dough Boy wear a hat?

3. On a standard paper clip, how many curves are there?

4. How many sides does a stop sign have?

5. On which playing card is the cardmaker's trademark?

6. What numbers on a telephone dial are not accompanied by a segment of the alphabet?

7. How many sides are there on a "No. 2" pencil?

8. On a standard traffic light, is the red on the top or bottom?

9. What building is on the back of a five-dollar bill?

10. Which way does Lincoln face on the penny?

POT SHOTS

Most car horns honk in F major.

•••

Frances Cleveland was the youngest First Lady-
21 years old.

ANSWERS

1. Red

2. Yes

3. Three

4. 8

5. Ace of spades

6. 1 and 0

7. Six

8. Top

9. The Lincoln Memorial

10. To the right

POT SHOTS

In an average lifetime, a person will grow
over six feet of nose hair.

•••

Pepsi Cola was first known as "Brad's Drink."

•••

Entomophagy is the name for insect eating.

DISNEY WHIRL

*Disney films have been a perennial favorite of kids of all ages.
Everybody knows characters like Snow White and Cinderella
but this quiz tests how well you know the supporting players.
Name the films in which you'd find these characters.*

1. Maleficent

2. Cooper

3. Flit

4. Admiral Boom

5. Merryweather

6. Yensid

7. Stinky Pete

8. Mushu

9. Zazu

10. Flower

POT SHOTS

Georgia has - or had - a law against saying
"Oh boy" in public.

•••

In *The Wizard of Oz*, Dorothy's last name is Gale.

ANSWERS

1. *Sleeping Beauty*

2. *The Fox and the Hound*

3. *Pocahontas*

4. *Mary Poppins*

5. *Sleeping Beauty* (one of the three good fairies)

6. *Fantasia* (the Sorcerer- "Disney" spelled backwards)

7. *Toy Story 2*

8. *Mulan* (guardian dragon)

9. *Lion King*

10. *Bambi* (the skunk)

PRIVIA

Actor/comedian Chevy Chase, born Cornelius Crane Chase, is heir to the Crane Urinal fortune so, as far as cash goes, you could say he is "flush."

———

Jodie Foster put her Oscar (for best actress) in her bathroom next to the tub.

CHEMISTRY TEST

What are the following common chemicals and compounds better known as?

1. Acetaminophen (Ah-seet-a-min-oh-fin)

2. Deoxyribonucleic Acid (Dee-oxee-rybo-new-clay-ic)

3. Ethylene Glycol (Eth-ell-een Gly-kol)

4. Trinitrotoluene (Try-nitro-tahl-uween)

5. Polytetrafluoroethylene

6. Calcium Sulphate Hemihydrate

7. Polyvinyl Chloride

8. Phylloquinone

9. Paradichlorobenzene

10. Ethanol

POT SHOTS

Superman's birthday is February 29th.

•••

The average office chair with wheels travels
8 miles per year.

•••

A goldfish can remember something for three seconds.

ANSWERS

1. Tylenol

2. DNA

3. Antifreeze

4. The common explosive TNT

5. Teflon

6. Plaster of Paris

7. PVC

8. Vitamin K

9. Moth balls

10. Alcohol

POT SHOTS

President John Quincy Adams owned a pet alligator.

•••

The place where more people are struck by lightning
than anywhere else? ... On a golf course.

•••

Don't you think there's something odd about the fact
that there's a town in Missouri called Peculiar?

ON THE LOOKOUT

1. Where could you find a fossorial animal?

2. Where might you see a kazatsky?

3. On what car would you see the Spirit of Ecstasy?

4. Where can you see Moses' Cows?

5. Where would you find *Arrangement In Black and Gray: The Artist's Mother*?

6. Where might you be if you happened upon a grundy or a vetch?

7. Where would you be if you were attending the National Ringer Bowl?

8. It's raining - if you wanted to find a "ferrule", where would you look?

9. "Crema" can commonly be seen …?

10. On what article of clothing might you find a "keeper"?

POT SHOTS

Ann-Margret's last name is Olsson.

•••

Jimmy Carter was the first U.S. president
born in a hospital.

•••

Fish can get seasick.

ANSWERS

1. Underground

2. In Russia ... It's the folk dance where the arms are folded and the knees are bent.

3. On the hood of a Rolls Royce

4. You can "spot" them in Israel ...That's what they call lady bugs.

5. In a frame ... it's the official title of *Whistler's Mother.*

6. At a Frisbee match

7. In Wildwood, New Jersey at the National Marbles Championships

8. The tip of an umbrella

9. Atop a cup of expresso ... it's the characteristic foam.

10. On a belt ... it's the loop that holds the loose end.

POT SHOTS

Tim Allen's real name is Tim Dick. (His middle name was Allen.)

•••

Oscar winner Tommy Lee Jones was ex-vice president Al Gore's college roommate at Harvard (class of '69).

BODY OF KNOWLEDGE

How much do you know about your body? Let's find out.

1. If you suffer from "borborygmi," what are you experiencing?

2. If a doctor uses the term "metopic," what's he referring to?

3. Every human cell has about eight feet of____?

4. The thigh bone may be connected to the knee bone but this bone ain't connected to any other bone.

5. If you get taresthesia, what should you do?

6. You carry it wherever you go and get a completely new one every four weeks. What is it?

7. You have a lot of them and they live about 150 days.

8. By what name do most people know the thyroid cartilage?

9. Your fingerprints are not the only things that are unique. What other body part makes a very unique print?

10. What is the hardest substance the body produces?

THOUGHTS OF THE THRONE

Then I go into the bathroom at the airport. Now, I don't know who designs and makes these decisions, but why is it that we're not allowed to have actual twist-on, twist-it-off faucets in the bathroom? Is is just too risky for the general public to be in charge of the water flow?

-Jerry Seinfeld

ANSWERS

1. A growling stomach

2. Your forehead

3. DNA

4. The Hyoid in the throat is a bone all alone.

5. Better shake a leg- your foot fell asleep.

6. Your top layer of skin

7. Eyelashes

8. The Adam's apple

9. Tongue

10. Tooth enamel

PRIVIA

38% of Americans sing in the shower (or bath).

———

A third of all Americans flush the toilet
while still sitting on it.

MAPPING IT OUT

*Let's hit the road and test our knowledge of U.S. geography.
Just keep in mind this is one of our tougher tests
so buckle up, you may be in for a bumpy ride.*

1. In 1993 the town of Ismay, Montana changed its name
   (on a part-time basis) to what household name?

2. You know the city nicknamed "The Big Apple" but how about
   the town dubbed "The Little Apple?"

3. This Florida town, translated in English, means "Rat's Mouth,"
   but you know it better by its Spanish name. What is it?

4. We're betting you can guess the state where the town of
   Jackpot is located.

5. What state would you fly out of if you wanted to leave the
   town of Moon?

6. If you were in the Jump Rope Capital of the World, where
   would you be?

7. Zurich, Holland and Denmark are countries but they are all
   also towns in what state?

8. Where would you find the country's only moving national
   monument?

9. If something ever happened to Washington D.C., where would
   the U.S. capital be moved?

10. True or false? St. Nicholas Church is located in Santa Claus,
    Indiana.

ANSWERS

1. It became Joe, Montana to honor the football star.

2. It's Manhattan, Kansas where the folks painted those words on their water tower.

3. Boca Raton

4. Nevada

5. Pennsylvania, just on the border of Pittsburgh

6. Bloomer, Wisconsin

7. Kansas

8. San Francisco (the cable cars)

9. Port Angeles, Washington as designated by Abraham Lincoln

10. True!

POT SHOTS

Thumbnails are the fastest growing fingernails.

•••

It was - and maybe still is - against the law to duck hunt from an airplane in Colorado.

•••

The average American has a 10,000 word vocabulary.

ALL-AMERICAN STUMPERS

1. Thumbs up if you can get this one: Twenty-eight-inch-tall Charles Stratton is better known by what nickname?

2. What nutty symbol was invented in 1916 by a Suffolk, Virginia schoolchild who won $5 in a contest?

3. Richard and Maurice had a restaurant in San Bernandino California in the '50s which was franchised by a paper cup and milk shake salesman. Any guesses as to what Richard and Maurice's last name was?

4. Back in the days before TV was served on satellite dishes, American TV dinners were served on foil trays. What company introduced this culinary convenience?

5. According to the directions, whose murder are you solving when you play a game of Clue?

6. Which was introduced first - baseball cards, the Yo-Yo or Silly Putty?

7. This television institution appeared first on April 3, 1953 and has been running ever since. What is it?

8. Pennsylvanian Carl E. Stotz made a small name for himself when he began this organization in 1939. What was it?

9. What product was originally called "Little Short-Cake Fingers?"

10. What two famous animal drawings did cartoonist Thomas Nast create?

ANSWERS

1. Tom Thumb

2. Mr. Peanut

3. They were the McDonalds and the salesman, Ray Kroc, became the founder of the world's largest restaurant chain.

4. Swanson, in 1954

5. Mr. Boddy's

6. Baseball cards ... They date back to 1900 while the Yo-Yo came along in 1929 and Silly Putty in 1945

7. *TV Guide*

8. Little League

9. Twinkies

10. The donkey for the Democratic Party and the elephant for the Republicans

POT SHOTS

John Hancock and Charles Thomson were the only two people who signed the Declaration of Independence on July 4th. Most of the signers didn't add their John Hancocks until August 2nd, and the last signature wasn't added until five years later.

AD-VERSITY.

Sure, we've all heard the ads but do you remember the products?

1. "Does she or doesn't she? Only her hairdresser knows for sure."

2. " I can't believe I ate the whole thing."

3. " A little dab'll do ya."

4. "I liked it so much I bought the company."

5. "How do you spell relief?"

6. "Inquiring minds want to know."

7. "Better living through chemistry."

8. " Promise her anything, but give her _____."

9. "From the land of sky blue waters."

10. "LSMFT"

POT SHOTS

Venetian blinds were invented by the Japanese,
English muffins were first made in America,
and India ink comes from China.

•••

Albert Einstein was 26 when he published his theory
of relativity.

•••

Donald Duck's nieces are April, May and June.

ANSWERS

1. Clairol

2. Alka-Seltzer

3. Brylcreem

4. Remington shavers

5. Rolaids

6. *The National Enquirer*

7. Dupont

8. Arpege

9. Hamm's Beer

10. "Lucky Strike Means Fine Tobacco"

THOUGHTS OF THE THRONE

Why do airlines put an oxygen mask directly over your seat? You don't need it there. You know where they should put it? Inside the tiny little bathroom. That's where you need the oxygen.

-Jay Leno

NOTABLE QUOTABLES

Who is best known for saying the following?

1. "Mr. Watson, come here."

2. "Never have so many owed so much...."

3. "And that's the way it is."

4. "No one ever went broke underestimating the taste of American people."

5. "A penny saved is a penny earned."

6. "Reports of my death have been greatly exaggerated."

7. "I never met a man I didn't like."

8. "This is another fine mess you've gotten me into."

9. "It's not easy being green."

10. "The answer my friend is blowin' in the wind."

POT SHOTS

Robin Williams was voted "least likely to succeed" in high school.

•••

While on his honeymoon in 1879, Robert Louis Stevenson wrote *Travels With a Donkey*. Naturally, his wife was flattered.

ANSWERS

1. Alexander Graham Bell

2. Winston Churchill

3. Walter Cronkite

4. H.L. Mencken

5. Benjamin Franklin

6. Mark Twain

7. Will Rogers

8. Oliver Hardy

9. Kermit the Frog

10. Bob Dylan

POT SHOTS

A grasshopper can jump about two feet.

•••

Smile and your
Levator Labii Superioris Alaque Nasi smiles with you.
It's one of the primary muscles used for smiling.

•••

Thomas Jefferson invented the first hideaway bed.

FACTOID OR FALSEHOOD?

1. According to a Gallup poll, the most despised household task is cleaning the bathroom.

2. Your birthday is not a special day after all—you share it with no fewer than nine million others.

3. The average person will catch 50 colds in a lifetime.

4. The odds against flipping a coin heads up 10 times in a row are 1,023 to 1.

5. It takes 17 muscles to smile and 43 to frown.

6. The average American will eat 35,000 cookies during their lifetime.

7. The average person blinks 25 times per minute, which works out to about 13,140,000 blinks each year.

8. The sun is about 10 times larger than Earth.

9. The sound of a snore (up to 69 decibels) can be almost as loud as a pneumatic drill (70-90 decibels).

10. The study of population statistics is called statology.

PRIVIA

Leave it to Beaver was the first television program to show a toilet on TV.

ANSWERS

1. False ... Washing the dishes far outweighs its closest competitor with 17 percent of the voting. Second, at 8.8 percent was cleaning the bathroom.

2. True

3. False ... The average American catches 140 colds in a lifetime.

4. True

5. True ... so cheer up!

6. True

7. True

8. False ... It's more like 330,000 times larger.

9. True

10. False ... It's demography.

POT SHOTS

Bugs Bunny was first called Happy Rabbit.

•••

Portland is the largest city in both Maine and Oregon.

•••

The microwave oven is used more for reheating coffee than for any other reason.

WHAT THE ... ?

The following all have something in common.
Your job, should you decide to accept it and not just skip on
to the next quiz, is to figure out what it is. Good luck.

1. The spiny cheek, starsnout poacher, and monkeyface prickleback are all names of _____.

2. Aubergine, brinjal and melanzana are also names of _____.

3. The Basenji, Borzoi and the Vizsla are all _____.

4. Where would you find borsolinos, porkpies and panamas?

5. What would you be doing if you were using chervil, cardamon and turmeric?

6. Where would you be if you were in Cucumber, Duck or Pie?

7. Little Larry, Puny Pete, and Small Sam were all _____.

8. Who are Pipeye, Peepeye, Pupeye, and Poopeye?

9. What do Thomas Jefferson Snodgrass, Sergeant Fathom, and W. Apaminondas Adrastus Blab have in common?

10. Crumb box, brain wagon, bazoo wagon, strawberry patch, and loose cage are all names given to _____.

PRIVIA

A German toilet paper maker manufactured a brand of paper imprinted with a 26-lesson language course in English.

ANSWERS

1. Fish

2. Eggplants

3. Breeds of dogs

4. On your head ...They are all hats.

5. Cooking ... They're spices.

6. West Virginia

7. Names considered by Charles Dickens for the character Tiny Tim

8. Popeye's nephews

9. They are the names Samuel Clemens considered before deciding on Mark Twain.

10. A railroad caboose

PRIVIA

When Josephy Gayetty invented toilet paper in 1857, he had his name printed on each sheet.

———

Elvis Presley had a reading chair in his bathroom.

SHINING STARS

Everybody has to start somewhere.
Even the most glamorous career has humble beginnings.
Match the celebrity with the job he or she held before making it big.

1. Sean Connery	a) Lion cage cleaner
2. Martin Sheen	b) Secretary
3. Quentin Tarentino	c) Truck driver
4. Kris Kristofferson	d) Video store clerk
5. k.d. Lang	e) Photojournalist
6. Candice Bergen	f) Coffin polisher
7. Barbara Walters	g) Carpenter
8. Harrison Ford	h) Pilot
9. Sylvester Stallone	i) Fruit picker
10. John Wayne	j) Professional caddy

POT SHOTS

The name of the dog shown
on a Cracker Jack box is Bingo.

•••

According to *Harper's Index*, 80 percent
of Americans believe in miracles.
(The other 20 percent have been audited.)

ANSWERS

1. F

2. J

3. D

4. H

5. C

6. E

7. B

8. G

9. A

10. I

POT SHOTS

Sports superstars have been honored by having their number retired. You, too, will have your day in glory. Your social security number will be permanently retired on the day you die.

•••

Michaelangelo's last name was Buonarroti.

HAVE YOU HERD?

*It may seem that the many unique terms for groups of animals
were created merely for the benefit of trivia book writers.
You'll get no argument here. Match 'em up.*

1. Turtles	a)	Knot
2. Goldfinches	b)	Troop
3. Toads	c)	Bard
4. Whales	d)	Dray
5. Sheep	e)	Float
6. Squirrels	f)	Smack
7. Kangaroos	g)	Charm
8. Jellyfish	h)	Quiver
9. Crocodiles	i)	Drove
10. Cobras	j)	Gam

POT SHOTS

"Chop suey" means "odds and ends."

•••

A watermelon is 92 percent water.

•••

Gorillas can't swim.

ANSWERS

1. C

2. G

3. A

4. J

5. I

6. D

7. B

8. F

9. E

10. H

POT SHOTS

General George Custer achieved a rather dubious
distinction for his last stand at Little Big Horn.
That wasn't his only last - Custer finished at the
bottom of the 35 student graduating class
of West Point in 1861.

LADY BE GOOD

Here's some "Lady" trivia- just don't expect any help from Lady Luck.

1. The first lady's boot was designed for what royal figure? (Hint: We're having a hard time keeping it a "secret.")

2. Two canine heroes combined to form the title of what 1955 Walt Disney flick?

3. *My Fair Lady* was the collaborative effort of which composers?

4. Who was First Lady Patricia Nixon's guest that caused the secret service radio trouble?

5. What Lady was paid tribute by chocolatier Joseph Draps in 1926?

6. Who was the first First Lady to vote in a presidential election?

7. The most distinctive jazz/blues singer of her time, her real name was Eleanor Fagan. Her nickname was "Lady Day." Can you identify her?

8. Harriet Lane, although not his wife, took on the role of First Lady for which President?

9. Before becoming a First Lady she was known as Claudia Alta Taylor. Who is she better known as?

10. Who was the first presidential wife to be called the First Lady?

POT SHOTS

Men are more likely to be colorblind than women.

ANSWERS

1. Queen Victoria in 1840

2. *Lady and the Tramp*

3. Playwright and lyricist Alan Jay Lerner and Frederick Loewe

4. Big Bird ... When *Sesame Street's* Big Bird visited the White House, the Secret Service's radio frequency got mixed up with Big Bird's microphone frequency - so the Secret Service was picking up Big Bird's lines in their earpieces.

5. Godiva Chocolates were launched in 1926 in Brussels, Belgium. The chocolate company was named in honor of the 1040 A.D. legend, Lady Godiva.

6. Eleanor Roosevelt ... It is presumed that she voted for her husband, Franklin, who was on the ballot in 1920 for U.S. vice president.

7. Billie Holiday

8. James Buchanan ... He was the only president of the United States never to marry. During his term in office, his niece served in the capacity of First Lady.

9. Lady Bird Johnson

10. Mary Todd Lincoln

POT SHOTS

The average American generates three pounds of garbage a day.

PRESIDENTIAL POSERS

1. The thirtieth president of the U.S. was born on July 4, 1872. Who is he?

2. Who was the only president elected unanimously?

3. What is the largest mausoleum in North America?

4. Which 20th century president's middle name was Gamaliel?

5. Which two presidents had double letters in both their first and last names?

6. Who is William Jefferson Blythe IV?

7. What president's daughter had a horse named Macaroni which she rode around the White House Lawn?

8. Four state capitals are named after presidents. Can you name them?

9. Thelma Catherine Ryan had a cameo role in the 1935 movie *Becky Sharp* but her scene was edited out of the film. She moved on to another scene, the nation's capital, as the wife of which president?

10. Who were the tallest and shortest presidents?

PRIVIA

When Sir Winston Churchill lost his seat in Parliament, someone saw fit to cable this message to him: "What good is a W.C. without a seat?"

ANSWERS

1. Calvin Coolidge

2. George Washington, who ran unopposed for both of his terms.

3. Grant's Tomb, in New York City ... Ulysses S. and wife Julia Dent Grant are buried there.

4. Warren G. Harding

5. William Harrison and Millard Fillmore

6. Bill Clinton ... That was his name at birth.

7. John F. Kennedy's daughter, Caroline

8. Jackson, Mississippi; Jefferson City, Missouri; Lincoln, Nebraska; and Madison, Wisconsin

9. Richard Nixon ... Thelma Catherine Ryan was Pat Nixon's maiden name.

10. 6'4" Abraham Lincoln was the tallest. At 5'4" in height, James Madison was the smallest president.

POT SHOTS

There's a town called Leap, Oregon, which was named in - you guessed it - a leap year.

•••

A man with more than one wife is a polygamist. A woman with more than one husband is a polyandrist.

ODD JOBS

*Should you land any one of the following jobs
what exactly would you be doing?*

1. Scarpologist

2. Whirly Girl

3. Clack

4. Brontologist

5. Funambulist

6. Piscatologist

7. Etymologist

8. Pugilist

9. Perfusionist

10. Enologist

POT SHOTS

Aspirin was invented in Germany in 1853
but not marketed until 1899.
Take two and call me in 46 years!

•••

The White House is the most visited home
in the United States. Second is Graceland,
the former home of Elvis.

ANSWERS

1. You'd be into the science of determining characteristic traits by examining a person's shoes.

2. You'd be working for, or be a member of, the International Association of Women Helicopter Pilots.

3. You're one of a group of people hired to applaud a performance.

4. You'd be studying the science of thunder.

5. You're a tight rope walker.

6. Your work entails the science of fish.

7. You're into the origin and development of words.

8. You're into rings- boxing rings. A pugilist is a fighter.

9. You're the one who runs the heart-lung machine.

10. This one's at the bottom of the list, or the cellar, that is. You're a wine expert.

PRIVIA

The National Aeronautics and Space Administration spent $23 million to build a prototype toilet for the space shuttle. The cost represented a 900 percent increase over the original estimate because the astronauts wanted a manual flush rather than an automatic one. Talk about true government waste!

10 FOR THE ROAD

Time to rally your memories and match the date with the event.

1. First gas pump installed in the U.S.   a) 1935

2. First use of tar as a road surface   b) 1980

3. U.S. license tag standardized   c) 1922

4. First U.S. toll road   d) 1899

5. First parking meter   e) 1792

6. First million-selling vehicle   f) 1914

7. Word "petrol" coined   g) 1906

8. Japanese auto production overtakes U.S.   h) 1902
   production for the first time
                                                               i) 1957
9. First electric traffic light
                                                               j) 1958
10. Day-night rearview mirror introduced

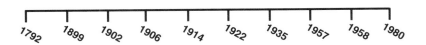

1792   1899   1902   1906   1914   1922   1935   1957   1958   1980

POT SHOTS

September is the month with the highest birthrate.

ANSWERS

1. G

2. H

3. I

4. E

5. A

6. C (The Model T)

7. D

8. B

9. F

10. J

POT SHOTS

A numerym is a word for a phone number
that spells a word.

•••

Lefties get injured more often than right-handed
people. And, in fact, more than 2,500 southpaws
die each year using products meant
for right-handed people.

THE LAY OF THE LAND

Are you a geography whiz? Try this quiz.

1. The states of Alaska and New Hampshire sit at opposite ends of the spectrum when it comes to what?

2. What sizeable city always celebrates Halloween on October 30th?

3. Which state has a much longer name than is commonly known?

4. Who owns about a third of all the land in the United States?

5. What state would you travel to in order to find Pittsburg?

6. What common bond do Virginia, Pennsylvania, Kentucky and Massachusetts have?

7. How many U.S. states border the Pacific Ocean?

8. What famous landmark and attraction would you find in California's Balboa Park?

9. The State of New York is distinct among all state names. What's so special about it?

10. If you're heading south from Detroit, Michigan, what's the first foreign country you come to?

THOUGHTS OF THE THRONE

The Rose Bowl is the only bowl I've ever seen that I didn't have to clean.

-Erma Bombeck

ANSWERS

1. Length of coastlines ... Alaska has the longest and New Hampshire has the shortest.

2. Carson City- October 31st is reserved as Nevada Day.

3. Rhode Island which is officially Rhode Island and Providence Plantations

4. The Federal government

5. Either Texas, California, Oklahoma, Kentucky or New Hampshire - In Pennsylvania, it's Pittsburgh with an "h."

6. Technically, they are not states but Commonwealths.

7. Five ... Did you forget Alaska and Hawaii?

8. The San Diego Zoo

9. It's the only state that ends with the letter "k."

10. Canada- and it won't take long at all.

POT SHOTS

If you're going to be doing something "in a jiffy," you'd better hurry up. A jiffy is 1/100th of a second.

•••

Benjamin Franklin invented Daylight Savings Time.

•••

Dolly Parton once lost a Dolly Parton look-alike contest.

COMMERCIAL ARTISTS

1. Julianna Margulies, best known from TV's *ER*, has a noteworthy father. He was the ad executive that created a very popular jingle. What was it?

2. To help pay her college tuition, Susan Sarandon modeled for a brochure promoting what famous Washington, D.C. hotel?

3. In 1982, Sarah Michelle Gellar was in the first commercial ever that mentioned a competitor. Who was the commercial for and who was their rival?

4. Who did the voice-over for the Secret commercial with the line "Secret: Strong enough for a man but made for a woman?"

5. What actor was able to turn around a failing Japanese hair gel company by being their spokesperson?

6. Betty Furness became TV's highest-paid saleslady; for a decade, she pitched the merits of _____?

7. 20,000 commercials are made a year aimed at children. 7,000 alone are for what general product?

8. The first animated TV commercial was made in 1948 for a Colgate-Palmolive cleanser. It featured the jingle, "You'll stop paying the elbow tax when you start cleaning with _____. "

9. Can you name the Charmin toilet tissue spokesman?

10. When "Poppy" was first introduced in 1965, he became a marketing hit. Who is he better known as?

ANSWERS

1. Alka Seltzer's *Plop-Plop, Fizz-Fizz*

2. The Watergate Hotel

3. She appeared in a Burger King commercial claiming McDonald's burgers were "smaller" than their competitors. Consequently, the McDonald's company sued her as well as Burger King. Gellar couldn't eat at a McDonald's unless she was in disguise, due to truth in advertising (One of her commercial lines was "I only eat at Burger King.").

4. William H. Macy

5. Charles Bronson.

6. Westinghouse refrigerators

7. Cereals

8. Ajax

9. Mr. Whipple

10. The Pillsbury Doughboy

 ## THOUGHTS OF THE THRONE

According to statistics, a man eats a prune every twenty seconds. I don't know who this fella is, but I know where to find him.

-Morey Amsterdam

TRIVIA "TOON"-UP

Here are some more animated antics to jog your memory.

1. What happened to Wile E. Coyote on May 21, 1980?

2. Mel Blanc, the voice of Bugs Bunny, was allergic to what food?

3. What is Donald Duck's middle name?

4. What Flintstone cartoon character was left out of the Flintstone vitamin bottle?

5. Artist Bob Clampett created Bugs Bunny after seeing what actor in what movie?

6. What is the name of Woody Woodpecker's girlfriend?

7. What is Foghorn Leghorn's favorite song?

8. What was the occupation of Charlie Brown's dad?

9. Who is Sweet Polly Purebread?

10. What was the name of the Bumstead's dog in the *Blondie* cartoon ?

POT SHOTS

Robert Redford turned down the title role in
The Graduate, Bing Crosby nixed the opportunity
to play the detective Columbo, and Mickey Rooney
said no to playing Archie Bunker.

ANSWERS

1. He caught the Road Runner.

2. Carrots

3. Fauntleroy

4. Betty Rubble

5. Clark Gable munching a carrot in the movie *It Happened One Night*

6. Winnie

7. *Camptown Races*

8. Barber

9. Underdog's girlfriend

10. Daisy

PRIVIA

Liberace's Palm Springs home had a toilet made to look like a royal throne.

———

Tycoon Howard Hughes kept magazines and books in the bathroom where he scouted movie prospects. (He spent much time there, ailing from chronic constipation.)

ARE YOU GAME?

Think you have the monopoly on classic board game trivia knowledge?
Let's roll the dice and find out.

1. What property in Monopoly was misspelled for years?

2. What's the name of the top-hatted Monopoly Man?

3. In 1976, Neiman-Marcus offered a Monopoly set for $600 made out of what substance?

4. How much money does the bank come with?

5. What property is landed on most often?

6. What is the property most landed on in the British version?

7. How many Community Chest and Chance Cards are there?

8. How many houses and hotels are there in the game of Monopoly?

9. Due to the metal shortage during WWII, Monopoly tokens were made out of what?

10. In 1999, a new token was voted in. What was decided?

POT SHOTS

Zip-a-dee-doo-dah: To bankers, ZIP is an acronym for Zero Interest Payment ... To psychologists, ZIP is short for Zero Intelligence Potential ... To postal workers, ZIP stands for Zone Improvement Plan.

ANSWERS

1. Marven Gardens

2. Rich Uncle Pennybags

3. Chocolate

4. $15,140

5. Illinois Ave.

6. Trafalgar Square

7. 16 apiece

8. There are 32 houses and 12 hotels.

9. Wood

10. A sack of money

POT SHOTS

Your chances of being a guest on *The Tonight Show*
are 1 in 490,000
(somewhat better if you're already famous).

•••

Two-thirds of the world's lawyers
are in the good old US of A(ttorneys).

•••

The best selling prepared dessert in the world is Jell-O.

"SCHOLARSHIP" PAGEANTS

If you managed to pay attention through all the tears, sincere sentiments about ending world hunger and tight bathing suits, you might earn the crown in this beauty of a trivia quiz.

1. Who was named America's Junior Miss in 1963 even though the judges felt she was too serious and sophisticated to hold the title?

2. What TV anchor married a Miss South Dakota?

3. Who retired from competition after five wins as Mr. Universe as well as being crowned Mr. Olympia six consecutive years in a row?

4. Suzette Charles became Miss America when what celebrity was stripped of her crown?

5. Before she played Xena: Warrior Princess, Lucy Lawless held what crown?

6. What happened when they announced the name of the 1952 Mrs. America?

7. What happened when Phyllis George was crowned (hint, hint) Miss America in 1971?

8. In 1967, Bert Parks got over-enthusiastic while singing *There She is, Miss America*. He didn't realize what he'd done. What did he do?

9. Miss America 1959 married which Miss America host?

10. Was there ever a Miss America who held the title for two consecutive years?

ANSWERS

1. Diane Sawyer. Charmed by Sawyer's silly side, several judges changed their votes in her favor and she was named America's 1963 Junior Miss.

2. Tom Brokaw

3. Arnold Schwarzenegger was crowned Mr. Universe in 1967 at the age of 20, the youngest man ever to win the title. He also collected the titles of Mr. Europe and Best-Built Man of Europe, and also won the International Powerlifting Championship. His triumphs in the sport were so consistent (he won four more Mr. Universe titles and six consecutive Mr. Olympia titles) that Schwarzenegger retired after seven years because he felt he "wasn't giving others a chance to win."

4. Vanessa Williams

5. Mrs. New Zealand in 1989

6. When Mrs. New Jersey heard her name announced, she passed out cold on-stage. It took panicked pageant officials several minutes to revive her.

7. Her crown was not properly attached and it fell, smashing rhinestones all over the stage.

8. He yanked out the microphone cord. Unaware of the mishap, the emcee continued to croon into a dead mike, giving the first "mime" rendition of the famous song.

9. Gary Collins

10. Yes- Mary K. Campbell of Ohio in 1922 and 1923

POTTY-POURRI

1. So everyone knows Charles A. Lindbergh flew the Atlantic solo but who accomplished this feat over the much larger Pacific?

2. Where would you be likely to find an endoplasmic reticulum?

3. Who founded the Library of Congress?

4. What's the title of the National Anthem of Grenada?

5. What indispensable automotive innovation did Charles Kettering give the world?

6. True or False? On the back of a hundred dollar bill, the clock on Independence Hall reads 4:10.

7. If you were to encounter Cnidaria, where would you be?

8. What exactly is a Queen Alexandra's Birdwing?

9. What 1893 invention was originally known as "The Clasp Locker?"

10. On what hill was the battle of Bunker Hill fought?

PRIVIA

In the bowl games department, 23 people were hired simply to flush toilets at the Gator Bowl in Jacksonville, Florida just before Christmas in 1989. It was a preventative measure to keep the pipes from freezing.

ANSWERS

1. Sir Charles Kingsford-Smith made the run from Oakland to Brisbane in 1928, the year following "Lucky Lindy's" flight.

2. Inside a cell

3. Thomas Jefferson

4. It has no title.

5. No crank inventor, he gave the world the electric starter.

6. True

7. In or near the water because that's where you usually find jellyfish, anemonies and coral

8. The world's largest butterfly- wingspan about 1 foot

9. The zipper

10. Breed's Hill (The battle was *supposed* to be on Bunker Hill. Later on, Breed's Hill was renamed Bunker Hill).

PRIVIA

King Louis XIV of France supposedly took only three baths in his life and was forced into taking all three to remove the royal funk.

POTTY-POURRI

1. What modern-day staple did Henry Bradley whip up in 1871?

2. True or False? The Mako shark is the fastest fish in the sea.

3. Who are the only two men in the Baseball Hall of Fame who have nothing to do with the game?

4. The Interstate Highway System was established by this far-sighted President.

5. The average citizen of Denmark eats 29.5 pounds of this a year- the world's highest consumption. What is it?

6. Who was *Time* magazine's "Man Of The Year" in 1982?

7. True or false? The cars on the back of the $10 bill are all Fords.

8. To whom was the White House staff referring when they called the First Family "The Three Musketeers?"

9. What change was made to the American flag in 1959?

10. What performer once went under the name Walter Busterkeys?

POT SHOTS

Stephen King, Michael Douglas and Johnny Carson
were all gas station attendants ...
And Jay Leno waxed cars.

•••

Magician Harry Houdini made his final disappearing
act on Halloween in 1926.

ANSWERS

1. Margarine ... You can bet he made a lot of bread on that idea!

2. False ... The mako is second to the sailfish which has been clocked at over 68 m.p.h.

3. Abbott and Costello, for their *Who's on First?* routine

4. Between his leadership in WWII and this project you could say Dwight Eisenhower was a real "road warrior."

5. Candy ... This is why you never see a poor Danish dentist.

6. The computer

7. False ... The're just generic cars created by the engraver.

8. The Trumans

9. Two more stars were added as Alaska and Hawaii became states.

10. Liberace

POT SHOTS

Dwarf, dwell and dwindle are the only three words in the English language that begin with "dw."

•••

A group of flamingos is called a "pat."

•••

West Point originated class rings.

INITIAL REACTION

1. What do the initials M.G. on the famous British-made automobile stand for?

2. What do the initials H and R represent in the H&R Block income tax company?

3. For what "cuddly" reason did President Ulysses S. Grant change his name from Hiram Ulysses Grant?

4. Unlike other U.S. presidents, Jimmy Carter avoided using his initials. Why?

5. What do P.G. Wodehouse's initials stand for?

6. Winton was the birthplace of Australia's international airline, Qantas. What do the initals stand for?

7. Where did the word tip come from?

8. How did the band REO Speedwagon choose its unusual name?

9. What does the J.C. stand for in J.C. Penney?

10. What did the "S" in Harry S Truman stand for?

THOUGHTS OF THE THRONE

Who invented the brush they put next to the toilet? That thing hurts.

-Andy Andrews

ANSWERS

1. Morris Garage

2. Henry and Richard, the founders of the company

3. He didn't want to enter West Point with the initials H.U.G.

4. "J.C." is usually associated with Jesus Christ.

5. Pelham Grenville

6. Its name came from the initials of Queensland and Northern Territory Air Services.

7. It dates back to England several hundreds of years ago. When people traveled by stagecoach, they often sent a servant ahead to make arrangements for their arrival. The servant would give the service providers money "to insure promptness" which was shortened by the acronym "tip."

8. It's from an early 1900s flatbed truck. The letters "REO" are the initials of Ransom Eli Olds, "Father of the Automobile," who invented the Oldsmobile and was president of Reo Motor Vehicle Company from 1904 to 1924.

9. James Cash

10. Not at all like Harry, it stood for nothing.

POT SHOTS

When cartoonist Charles Schulz was in high school,
the yearbook staff turned down his offer to include
a few of his comic strips.

SPACE RACE

Are you astronaut material or just a space cadet? Find out with this star-studded quiz.

1. What was the first song to be performed in outer space?

2. John Denver wanted to go into space. What mission turned him down?

3. How long did America's first space flight, made by Alan Shepard, last?

4. True or False? Chuck Yeager appeared in the film *The Right Stuff*.

5. What was the original name of *Plan 9 from Outer Space*?

6. What place in the history of space does Charlie Walker hold?

7. Neil Armstrong put the first footprint on the moon in 1969. Who left the last footprint on the lunar surface in 1972?

8. Who was the first astronaut to orbit the earth, and for extra credit, who was second?

9. What is the only state to allow absentee voting from space?

10. True or false? No less than a dozen astronauts have walked on the moon.

POT SHOTS

The color red is not generally used in the packaging of ice cream because it reminds people of the heat.

ANSWERS

1. *Happy Birthday* was sung by the Apollo IX astronauts on March 8, 1969.

2. The 1986 Challenger Mission

3. 15 minutes and 22 seconds

4. True

5. Ed Wood's dreadful sci-fi *Plan 9 from Outer Space* (1958) was originally titled *Grave Robbers from Outer Space*.

6. He was the first fare-paying passenger aboard the space shuttle, in 1984. McDonnell Douglas paid for his ride to the tune of $66,000.

7. Gene Cernan

8. John Glenn was first, Scott Carpenter second.

9. Texas

10. True

POT SHOTS

George Washington earned $25,000 a year
as president of the U.S.

•••

New Jersey is the only state
with the letter "J" in its name.

FACTOID OR FICTITIOUS?

1. Jell-O once came in celery, coffee, cola and chocolate flavors.

2. *Today Show* celebrity Willard Scott was the original Ronald McDonald.

3. The sensation of "pins and needles" is never felt in people under twelve years old.

4. Bagpipes originated in the Middle East.

5. The highest point in Pennsylvania is lower than the lowest point in Colorado.

6. The first celebration of "The Fourth Of July" took place on the eighth of July.

7. Unlike FM broadcasts, AM radio waves keep circling the earth so it's possible to pick one up two or three days after it was broadcast.

8. All penguins live in Antarctica or surrounding waters.

9. Almost two billion candy canes are made every year.

10. The moon moves further away from earth every year. True or False?

PRIVIA

Virginia once had a law requiring all bathtubs
to be kept in the yard and not in the house.
Saturday night must've been a real hoot!

ANSWERS

1. True

2. True

3. False

4. True

5. True

6. True (It was the first public reading of the *Declaration of Independence.*)

7. False

8. False ... Some live further north, one species ranging up to the equator.

9. True

10. True- about an inch and a half- almost 4 feet further since we lasted visited in 1972

POT SHOTS

More shoplifters are caught in December
than any other month.

•••

"Jack" is the most common name in nursery rhymes.

FIRST THINGS FIRST - TAKE 2

1. What was Chuck Berry's first number one hit?
   a) *Roll Over Beethoven*   b) *Johnny B. Goode*   c) *Maybelline*
   d) *My Ding-a-Ling*

2. What was the first group to appear on Dick Clark's *American Bandstand*?
   a) Chordettes   b) Temptations   c) Moonglows   d) Five Satins

3. Who graced the first cover of *Rolling Stone Magazine* in 1967?
   a) Elvis   b) Mick Jagger   c) John Lennon   d) Mamas and Papas

4. He hosted *Saturday Night Live* when it made its debut on
   November 11, 1975.   a) George Kennedy   b) George Carlin
   c) John Travolta   d) Steve Martin

5. Who smiled back from the first cover of *People Magazine* in 1974?
   a) Paul Newman   b) Barbra Streisand   c) Mia Farrow
   d) Robert Redford

6. Who was the first female artist inducted into the Rock & Roll
   Hall of Fame in 1987?   a) Dionne Warwick   b) Diana Ross
   c) Carly Simon   d) Aretha Franklin

7. What star appeared as the first guest on *The Tonight Show* when
   Jay Leno took over in 1992?
   a) Billy Crystal   b) Steve Martin   c) Johnny Carson   d) Bill Murray

8. Who performed the first CD for commercial release in the USA?
   a) Frank Sinatra   b) Bruce Springsteen   c) The Rolling Stones
   d) Elton John

9. The character names Roy Hinkley and Jonas Grumby were first
   and last used in the premiere episode of what 1964 TV show?
   a) *The Beverly Hillbillies*   b) *Gilligan's Island*   c) *McHale's Navy*
   d) *Get Smart*

10. The first rock-musical opened at the Biltmore theater in 1968
    and was entitled: a) *Godspell*   b) *Children of a Lesser God*
    c) *Hair*   d) *Oh Calcutta*

ANSWERS

1 D

2. A

3. C

4. B

5. C

6. D

7. A

8. B

9. B (The Professor and Skipper)

10. C

POT SHOTS

The second man to walk on the lunar surface was
Buzz Aldrin. His mother's maiden name is Moon.

•••

A group of owls is called a "parliament." By the way,
the owl is a real bird-brain and not wise. Crows are
thought to be the smartest birds.

BODY LANGUAGE

Bodies- we all have one.
Let's see what your brain knows about its closest partner in life.

1. What's the common name for an anatomical juxtaposition of two orbicularis oris muscles in a state of contraction?

2. What's faster- a cough or a sneeze?

3. If you're a completely average Joe- or Jane- how many times a day does Nature call?

4. About how many new skins will a person grow in an average lifetime?
   a) 25   b) 200   c) 500   d) 1,000

5. Where would you find the only living tissue in the human body with no blood vessels?

6. What age group is only half as likely to catch a cold as teenagers?

7. About 40% of the average body is made up of what?

8. True or False? Pound for pound, the human body produces more heat than the sun.

9. Where would you find your opisthenar?

10. Should you be suffering from blepharospasms, what would you be seen doing?

THOUGHTS OF THE THRONE

Show me a nation whose national beverage is beer,
and I'll show you an advanced toilet technology.

-Paul Hawkins

ANSWERS

1. A kiss

2. A sneeze leaves a cough in the dust with a speed of over 100 mph compared to 60.

3. Six times a day

4. D

5. Covering the eye ... It's the cornea.

6. People over 50

7. Muscles

8. True- about five times as much

9. You should know it like the back of your hand because that's what it is.

10. Winking uncontrollably

POT SHOTS

Jack Nicholson single-handedly rescued five drowning people from the New Jersey surf back in the '50s.

•••

No word in the English language rhymes with month, orange, purple or silver.

PUPPY LOVE

Match the animal with its offspring.

1. Wolf   a) Joey

2. Beaver   b) Leveret

3. Falcon or Hawk   c) Whelp

4. Kangaroo   d) Kitten

5. Pigeon   e) Ephyra

6. Carp   f) Eyas

7. Hare   g) Shoat

8. Hog   h) Squab

9. Jellyfish   i) Fry

10. Oyster   j) Spat

POT SHOTS

Thomas Jefferson's last words were, "Is it the Fourth?" ... Jefferson died July 4th, 1826.

•••

Another U.S. president, John Adams, also died that very day.

ANSWERS

1. C

2. D

3. F

4. A

5. H

6. I

7. B

8. G

9. E

10. J

POT SHOTS

Every clown is unique. Their faces have to be painted
on an eggshell to be registered. When a clown dies,
his egg is buried with him, no doubt sunny-side up.

TOY TRIVIA

*Whether they're cherished memories of childhood
or things you still hide away and play with in your bedroom
when no one's around, toys hold a soft spot in our hearts.
Besides not leaving them all over the floor for people to trip on,
let's see what you know about these popular playthings.*

1. What's the name of the little boy on the Play-Doh can?

2. What's inside an Etch-a-Sketch?

3. Who created Lincoln Logs?

4. How many sticks are used to play Pick up Sticks?

5. What year did Mr. Potato Head first sprout?
   (Hint: "I Like Ike")

6. How many tiles are there in a game of dominoes?

7. Mattel made a line of "Simpson" figures. Which one was not a member of the family?

8. What was James Wright trying to create when he accidentally invented Silly Putty?

9. What toy was used by the U.S. military during World War II?

10. Charles Pajeau, a tombstone maker by profession, tinkered around and gave the world a far less grave product in 1914. What was it?

THOUGHTS OF THE THRONE

*I sometimes feel alone and insignificant, especially
when people turn out the lights in the bathroom.*

-Steven Wright

ANSWERS

1. Play-Doh Pete ... He made his first appearance in 1960, four years after Play-Doh came out.

2. Etch-a-sketches have always used a mixture of plastic beads and aluminum powder.

3. John Lloyd Wright, architect Frank Lloyd Wright's son ... He based his design on the foundation of his father's design for the Tokyo Imperial Hotel.

4. 50

5. 1952, the year Ike Eisenhower was elected president

6. 28

7. Nelson, the Bully

8. Synthetic Rubber

9. View-Master

10. Tinker toys

POT SHOTS

LifeSavers candy was invented the same year
the Titanic sank.

•••

First Lady Eleanor Roosevelt's maiden name
was Roosevelt.

TV TOWNS

As any couch potato knows, the setting of a TV series is an important element of the show. Think back to the classic shows below and try to identify its primary location.

1. *Roseanne*

2. *Wings*

3. *Simon and Simon*

4. *Mork And Mindy*

5. *I Dream of Jeannie*

6. *Northern Exposure*

7. *Father Knows Best*

8. *Leave It To Beaver*

9. *The Many Loves Of Dobie Gillis*

10. *The Adventures Of Ozzie And Harriet*

POT SHOTS

During mating, the female preying mantis chews her partner's head off.

•••

Beards are the fastest growing hairs on the human body. If the average man never trimmed his beard, by the time he was 70 it would be nearly 30 feet long.

ANSWERS

1. Lanford, IL
2. Nantucket, MA
3. San Diego, CA
4. Boulder, CO
5. Cocoa Beach, FL
6. Cicely, AK
7. Springfield (generic)
8. Mayfield
9. Central City
10. Hillsdale

PRIVIA

The Scott Paper Company once conducted a survey that had these findings:

Two-thirds of people with a master's or doctorate degree read in the bathroom.

Sixty percent preferred the toilet paper over the top, 29 percent hung their rolls under, and 7 percent could care less.

Seven percent admitted to stealing toilet paper from public bathrooms.

Twenty-seven percent complained about people who don't replace the roll when it runs out.

FOOD FOR THOUGHT

1. When someone says "pizza pie" why are they being redundant?

2. What cereal was originally called Elijah's Manna?

3. Food poisoning was at least a contributing cause of death for this U.S. president who fell ill after consuming bad shellfish. Can you name him?

4. If you asked for a Bolshoi Mak in Russia, what would you be ordering?

5. In the 1800s, Dr. Miles' Compound Extract of Tomato was sold as a medicine. What is it known as today?

6. What's the largest fruit crop in the world?

7. What was it that, during World War II, GIs called the "ham that failed the physical?"

8. With what dressing do the Japanese eat their french fries?

9. Philadelphia illustrator Grace Wiederseim is credited with drawing what two chubby-faced children in 1904?

10. Famous Last Meals: Who enjoyed four scoops of ice cream and 6 chocolate chip cookies as his last meal?

THOUGHTS OF THE THRONE

Separate bedrooms and separate bathrooms.

-Bette Davis, on the key to a good marriage

ANSWERS

1. Because "pizza" in Italian means "pie"

2. Post Toasties

3. Warren G. Harding

4. A Big Mac

5. Ketchup

6. Grapes

7. Spam

8. Mayonnaise

9. The Campbell Soup Kids

10. Elvis Presley

POT SHOTS

Hershey, Pennsylvania used to be known as Derry Church. Wonder if Derry Church Bars would ever have caught on?

•••

CHOICE COD - Hold this upside-down in front of the bathroom mirror and you'll see that the first two words of this item read the same.

THE FABULOUS '50S

1. After holding at the same price for 26 years, the price of this universally used item finally went up in 1958. (Here's a "brain teaser" of a hint: It goes around the world but stays in a corner.)

2. Elizabeth Edith Enke provided comedic and domestic support to a groundbreaking comedian who was one of the great pioneers of TV. Who was she?

3. True or false? Television's *Meet the Press* began its run in the '50s.

4. Federal minimum wage hit $1 per hour in what year?
   a) 1956 b) 1957 c) 1958 d) 1959

5. Which famous candy slogan was introduced in 1954 along with a new peanut variety of this popular sweet treat?

6. *The Sound of Music* opened on Broadway in what year?

7. In the '50s, this musical act was known as "Tom and Jerry". They did a bit better with a new decade and a new name. What was it?

8. A major styling change came about on almost all American cars in 1958. Can you shed any light on it?

9. Name the popular local show hosted by a virtual unknown that went national in 1957.

10. Who was the unsuccessful Democratic candidate for President in 1952 and 1956?

ANSWERS

1. A first-class postage stamp jumped from a penny to 4 cents.

2. Edie Adams who was married to Ernie Kovacs

3. False- it began in the '40s!

4. A

5. Peanut M&Ms hit the stores along with the slogan "Melts in your mouth, not in your hand."

6. 1959, starring Mary Martin

7. Simon and Garfunkel

8. They went from single to dual headlamps.

9. *American Bandstand*

10. Adlai Stevenson

POT SHOTS

At birth a hippopotamus weighs about 100 pounds.

•••

If you're cynophobic, you have a fear of dogs.

•••

Potato chips were invented in 1853 in Saratoga, New York by George Crum.

THE SENSATIONAL '60S

1. Of the '50s, '60s and '70s, which decade was longer?

2. Built in August of 1961, this turned out to be one of the most unpopular structures in history.

3. First played in 1967, this popular sporting event didn't get its current name until 1969.

4. A modified Lincoln Futura became one of the most famous vehicles in the sixties as....?

5. Very active in the 1960s, this politician garnered more votes in his career than any other before or since.

6. What kind of car did "The Little Old Lady From Pasadena" drive?

7. The law that required cigarette manufacturers to put health warnings on their packages was enacted in what year?

8. The 1967 World's Fair was hosted by what North American city?

9. Who first appeared on the *Ed Sullivan Show* on February 9, 1964 and, according to Nielsen figures, attracted 73,700,000 viewers?

10. Name the classic action toy which made its first appearance at the American International Toy Fair in 1964.

ANSWERS

1. The '60s as it contained three leap years- '60, '64 and '68.

2. The Berlin Wall

3. The Super Bowl

4. The Batmobile

5. Richard Nixon (adding all the votes from his Presidential, Vice-Presidential, and various other elections)

6. A shiny red super-stock Dodge

7. 1965

8. Montreal- it was also known as "Expo 67."

9. The Beatles

10. G.I. Joe

POT SHOTS

DlanoD sivaD sdloh eht drocer rof gninnur eht
s'dlrow tsetsaf elim sdrawkcab, 6 setunim, 7 sdnoces.
(Yes, there's a reason why the words
in the previous sentence are in reverse.)

THE "ME" DECADE

1. Who won an Olympic record seven gold medals in 1972?

2. What was the most momentous event of August 9, 1974?

3. What was the biggest box office hit of 1975?

4. What famous baseball player died in a plane crash in 1972?

5. On *Happy Days*, what was the name of Howard and Marion Cunningham's bowling team?

6. The world was changed forever in 1977 as what new product went on sale for the first time?

7. What was the first year to celebrate Earth Day?

8. What baseball player had a candy bar named after him in 1978?

9. The last of the original three Stooges, Moe, died in 1975. What were Moe, Larry and Curly's last names?

10. What pet did Gary Dahl introduce in 1975?

PRIVIA

According to *Modern Bathrooms*, the most popular decoration on top of a toilet tank is scented seashells. Of course, we bathroom book publishers beg to differ.

ANSWERS

1. Mark Spitz

2. Richard Nixon resigned as president of the United States.

3. *Jaws*

4. Roberto Clemente

5. The Tenpins

6. The first personal computer, the Apple II

7. 1970

8. The "Reggie!" was named for Reggie Jackson ... Unlike the slugger, it didn't score and struck out in 1980.

9. Moe Howard, Larry Fine and Curly Howard

10. The pet rock

POT SHOTS

The maximum number of letters on one line of a *Wheel of Fortune* game board is 13.

•••

A regular sized Slinky has eighty feet of wire.

•••

The butterfly is a cannibal.

LAST CALL

1. The Beatles performed their last concert August 29, 1966
   in what city?
   a) Chicago   b) New York   c) San Francisco   d) Los Angeles

2. The last major silent movie ever made was _____?
   a) *Safety Last* b) *The Four Feathers* c) *The General*
   d) *Tilley's Punctured Romance*

3. The last _____ rolled off the assembly line August 19, 1958.
   a) Norge Refrigerator   b) Philco TV   c) LaSalle   d) Packard

4. What is Madonna's last name?
   a) Maloney   b) Ciccone   c) Clooney   d) Manana

5. When the NFL holds it annual draft, what is the nickname
   given to the football player selected last?
   a) Mr. Irrelevant   b) Mr. Can't Miss Pick   c) Mr. Nobody
   d) Mr. Fuhgeddaboutit

6. The final episode of what TV show was broadcast
   February 28, 1983?
   a) *Gilligan's Island*   b) *Taxi*   c) *Happy Days*   d) M*A*S*H

7. Who was Marilyn Monroe's last husband?   a) Joe DiMaggio
   b) Arthur Miller   c) Jimmy Dougherty   d) Ted Kennedy

8. What was used for the last time in Wimbledon '87?
   a) Line judges   b) Astro turf courts   c) Wooden tennis rackets
   d) Colored tennis balls

9. What was the last commissioned battleship?
   a) U.S.S. Arizona   b) H.M.S. Vanguard   c) U.S.S. Missouri
   d) I.J.N. Yamato

10. Last but not least, what is the fear of being last called?
    a) Lastaphobia   b) Endaphobia   c) Telesphobia   d) Ectophobia

ANSWERS

1. C

2. B

3. D

4. B

5. A

6. D

7. B

8. C

9. B

10. C

POT SHOTS

In the holiday song *The Twelve Days of Christmas*, there are a total of 364 gifts.

•••

Coca-Cola was originally green.

•••

21% of us don't make our bed on a daily basis.

BOWL GAMES

*Okay, here's where we take our final pot shots
with these bathroom-related questions.*

1. True or false? The White House had a telephone before it had indoor plumbing.

2. What's the most popular toothbrush color?

3. "It kills germs by the millions on contact" is the slogan of what mouthwash?

4. What singing artist made the 1970 recording of *She Came in Through the Bathroom Window*?

5. What famous painting did Francis I of France purchase in 1517 to hang in his bathroom?

6. What's the average lifespan of a bathroom scale?
   a) 5 years   b) 10 years   c) 15 years   d) 20 years

7. What comedienne and talk show host, whose real name is Joan Alexandra Molinsky, once said, "I knew I was unwanted when I saw that my bath toys were a toaster and a radio?"

8. What bigoted sitcom character said, "There's (sic) three things I hate: the opera, the police station and cold toilet seats."

9. Do you recall the name of J.P. "Big Bopper" Richardson's 1960 hit song that was inspired by a Dove soap commercial?

10. True or false? In 1878, Harley Procter got divine inspiration for the name "Ivory Soap" while he was sitting in church listening to a passage from the Bible about "ivory palaces."

ANSWERS

1. True

2. Blue

3. Listerine

4. Joe Cocker

5. *The Mona Lisa*

6. B

7. Joan Rivers

8. Archie Bunker

9. *Running Bear* (No, not Running *B-a-r-e*)

10. True ... Amen!

POT SHOTS

All llamas have bad breath - probably from yakking too much!

•••

Rattlesnakes gather in groups of up to a thousand to sleep through the winter.